Daisy Lane Home–School Read

In the shed

by Carol Matchett

Schofield & Sims

Dad was in the shed.

Jazz went in.

LAWN food
Tomato
COMPOST

Ollie went in.

Lawn food
Tomato
COMPOST
peas

A mouse went in.

Peas

Salt and Pepper went in.

Peas

A dog went in.

They all ran out!

Notes for parents and other helpers

Enjoying and talking about the story

CLL 1 listening and responding to stories; **CLL 2** linking events; **CLL 4** understanding stories

- Remember that the most important thing is to have fun and enjoy the story!
- Make sure that you are both in the mood for a story before you begin.
- Read the title and talk about the cover. **'Who is that in the shed? I wonder what the person is doing?'** Build up a sense of anticipation and eagerness before you start reading.
- Remember that the pictures are just as important as the words. Talk about what is happening in each picture. Some pages have no words, but you can talk about them: for example, **'What's happening in the picture? What is Jazz doing in the shed? What about the mouse?'**
- Remember to ask 'Why?' as well as 'What?' **'Why does Ollie go into the shed? Why do the cats go in?'**
- Use your voice to build up the anticipation of what might happen as each of the animals enters the shed (pages 7, 9 and 11).
- It's good to encourage the child to guess what might happen next. Try this before turning to page 12. **'I wonder what will happen now …'**
- Enjoy the ending. Show how to react to the events. **'Oh no! Look what has happened to the leaves!'** (page 13). Encourage the child to join in: **'I wonder what's happened to the mouse?'**
- Point out what happens in the next-door garden (pages 2, 3, 5, 12, 13).
- Relate the story to things the child has done at home, in the park or at nursery school: for example, helping in the garden, making piles of leaves or planting things. Discuss the behaviour of cats and dogs.

Book knowledge

CLL 4 knowing about books and print

- When you are reading the story, talk about what you are doing. Show the child the cover and how to turn the pages and read the words.
- Use words like **'cover'**, **'front'**, **'back'**, **'pages'**, **'words'** and **'pictures'**.
- Ask the child to help you to read the story. He or she can hold the book or turn the pages for you or point to where you should start reading.
- Point to the words as you read them aloud. This shows that, in English, print is read from left to right.
- Occasionally ask the child to do the pointing for you. Don't worry if he or she gets it wrong. Just show the child again how you do it and get on with the story.

First words

CLL 4 reading familiar words

- Don't rush this. Wait until the child is showing an interest in words and the print in books. He or she should *want* to have a go, not be forced to.
- Make sure that the child understands the idea of words. That's why pointing to words as you read them is important. But make sure that you still read the story properly and with expression ... don't read like a robot!
- The following commonly-used words appear repeatedly in this book and you should check that the child is beginning to recognise them: **'in'**, **'a'**, **'the'**, **'went'**.
- Draw particular attention to the words that are the same on each page – **'went'**, **'in'**.
- Ask the child to find the words **'went'** or **'in'** on each page.
- The repeated pattern in this story will help the child to predict the word coming next. Pause occasionally and ask the child to 'read' the next word: (page 7) **'A mouse went __'**.
- Give lots of praise.
- Point out the names of the characters on pages 2, 3, 5 and 9.
- When the child is familiar with the story, he or she might want to have a go at reading it. You can help him or her with the difficult parts, such as pages 2 and 13, where new words and/or ideas are introduced.
- Don't worry if the child says something wrong, as long as it makes sense. Give the child lots of praise for having a go.

Language development

CLL 1 extending vocabulary; using spoken language

- Talk about the items that you can see in the shed and in the garden.
- Talk about what is happening in the pictures, and respond to the things that the child notices. For example, if the child says (page 7) *'Look at the mouse'*, you could say: **'Yes, he's sniffing around on the floor. What do you think he's looking for?'** This opens the door for the child to think more and say more.
- Talk about familiar outdoor activities, such as sweeping leaves, planting things, mowing the grass and hanging out washing. If you have a garden, remind the child of the story when you are doing some of these things.

Retelling the story

CLL 4 retelling narratives

- Once the story is familiar let the child tell it in his or her own words. Don't worry about reading the actual words on the page. Let the child tell the story in his or her own way.
- Let the child turn over the pages, using the pictures to help retell the events in order.

Note for schools and nurseries

Each set of activities outlined above relates to the area of learning described as 'Communication, Language and Literacy' (CLL), as set out in the document *Curriculum guidance for the Foundation Stage* (Qualifications and Curriculum Authority, 2000). The aspects of learning covered by **Daisy Lane Home–School Readers** are as follows:

CLL 1 Language for communication
CLL 2 Language for thinking
CLL 3 Linking sounds and letters
CLL 4 Reading